Dedicated To:

To Maddy and Cole. Everything I do is for you. **Always dream bigger!**

To the people who made all of this happen in the first place, **Dane Best and the Best Family** (**Brooke, Derrick, Colby and Dax**).
Thank you for allowing me into your family and for the opportunity to share Dane's story with the world.
Dane, never stop stepping up and giving young people a voice. This is only the start of your story.
Don't forget me when you run for President. I think there's a book for that as well.

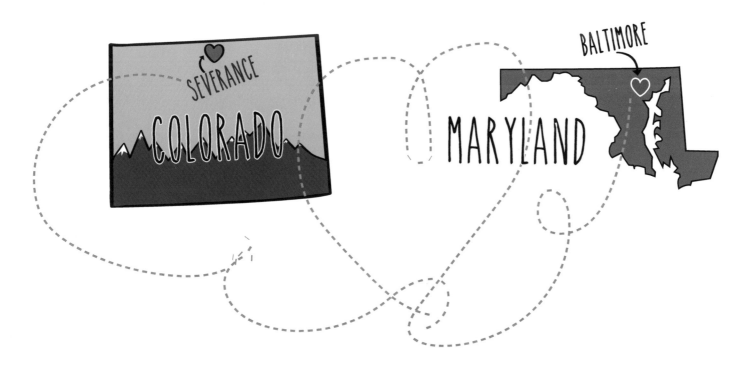

The Omnibus Publishing
5422 Ebenezer Rd.
POB 152
Baltimore, MD 21162
www.theomnibuspublishing.com

Book Layout ©2019 - Cover Design by Richie Frieman

Ordering Information:

Quantity sales. Special discounts are available on quantity purchases by schools, corporations, associations, and others. For details, contact the "Special Sales Department" at the address above.

Snowballs for Severance The Terrifically True Story of Dane Best and the Snowball Ban / Richie Frieman. 1st ed.

ISBN 978-1-7335985-1-4 / Library of Congress Control Number: 2019936540 - CIP Data available from Library of Congress

The illustrations is this book were done in digital format by Richie Frieman.

SNOWBALLS FOR SEVERANCE

THE TERRIFICALLY TRUE STORY OF DANE BEST AND THE SNOWBALL BAN

WRITTEN & ILLUSTRATED BY RICHIE FRIEMAN

My name is Dane Best. I'm nine years old and live in the quiet, snowy town of Severance, Colorado. Smack dab in the middle of Severance is my school, Range View Elementary. Hundreds of kids come together here every day to learn, have fun, and enjoy being a kid.

One day during a school field trip to the Severance Town Hall, I learn something about Severance. A thing so big, it goes completely against being a kid and having fun.

I have no idea, but this particular field trip will change my life forever.

I walk with my classmates and my mom, who is a chaperone for the day, to Mayor Don McLeod's office in Town Hall.

"What do you think you'll learn today, Dane?" Mom asks.

"I don't know, but hopefully there's pizza. Do you think there will be pizza?" I ask excitedly.

"Glad to see that's what you're hoping for today, Dane," she says.

"Laugh now Mom, but if there is pizza you'll be just as happy," I reply.

"Goooooood morning, Range View Elementary! I'm Mayor McLeod and I'll be your host for the day," he says.

"Do you think he's the one who hands out the pizza?" I whisper to Mom.

She rolls her eyes at me.

"Today, I'll take you around to different stations and explain how Severance keeps the town clean and safe, as well as discuss our laws."

Ugh. Zero mention of pizza, I think to myself.

The first station talks about how laws are made.

"Here, the town Trustees gather to oversee and discuss our laws. Can anyone name a law we have in Severance?" Mayor McLeod asks.

One of my classmates raises their hand and says, "No speeding."

"You're correct! That's why there are speed limit signs all across town."

Mayor McLeod adds, "Speeding is one example; however, did you know in Severance you're only allowed to have three pets? They can't be gerbils, chickens, or guinea pigs."

"Wait, no guinea pigs? Are they going to take ours away from us, Mom?"

"No, Dane. She will be fine."

"Gosh, what's next? No candy on Halloween or something?" I ask her.

Before she can answer me, Mayor McLeod asks our class another question.

"Since it's winter, did you know there is a law that bans snowball fights in Severance?"

Hold up. Did I just hear him say there's a law against snowball fights? I mean, the three pets thing is whacko for sure, but no snowballs in Severance? What planet am I on?

The mayor continued his talk, "Passed around 1920, the law states you can't throw projectiles that could hurt someone. Since a snowball is something that you could throw at someone, it's also included."

What's next, banning water balloon and pillow fights?

"*This can't be real, can it?* " I say to Mom.

"He's correct, Dane. You can't throw snowballs in Severance."

"The law was made around 1920. That's like a bazillion years ago. That's even older than you, Mom!"

"Yes, Dane. It may be shocking to hear but there are laws, and other things for that matter, that are older than Mom and Dad."

"**HELLOOOOOOO**, we live in Colorado! It snows here all the time. I mean, snow is what we're known for, Mom. Plus, snowball fights are a major part of being a kid."

I think about all the amazingly-awesome things I do when it snows. When I see the very first snowflake fall from the sky, I get super excited! I can't wait to run outside and breathe in the fresh winter air. I love sliding into a pile of snow like a baseball player diving into home plate. My older brother, Colby, and my younger brother, Dax, spend hours with me racing down steep hills on our sleds and building snowmen.

Finally, when we're too tired to move, we lay back and let the snowflakes fall on to our faces.

SLEDDING SNOWMEN
SKIING SNOWBALLS

THAT'S WHAT WINTER IS ALL ABOUT

The rest of the field trip is a complete blur. Oh, and there is no pizza, in case you are wondering. For whatever reason, I can't stop thinking about the town's snowball ban.

Why has no one ever tried to change it?

Every other kid, in every other town, in every other state gets to throw snowballs, except for kids in Severance.

THAT'S CRAAAAAAAAAZY!

How am I the only one who thinks this is bizarre? Then it hit me. What if I'm not the only one? Maybe my friends will agree that the snowball ban is unfair?

After school, I tell my dad about the field trip to Town Hall.

"Dad, do you know about the goofy Severance snowball ban?"

"Sure! It's a little odd I guess. However, it's a law and we have to follow it."

"Well, I for one think it's ridiculous," I tell him.

"Maybe when you're older, you can make and change laws that you think are best for the town," he replies.

I think about how long it will take for me to be "older" in order to change the snowball ban. Older like being an adult? That kind of older? Yikes!

Oh no, I don't have time to wait until I'm older. I need to do something about this ASAP.

I zip past my dad, and straight to my bedroom.

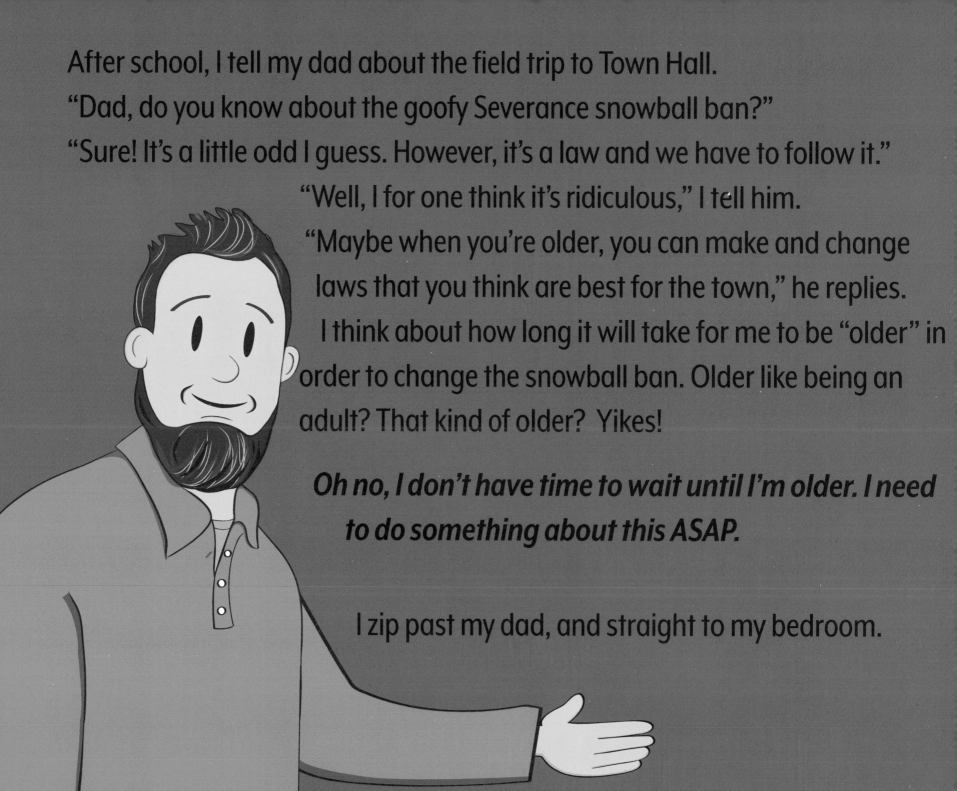

"What's with the rush, Dane?"

"Sorry. I can't talk now. My brain is in overdrive."

"Overdrive? About what?"

"The snowball ban. It's silly and outdated," I say, keeping my face buried in my work. "Mayor McLeod said the Trustees discuss the laws and this law needs a major discussion. I'm going to do something about it."

"Okaaaaaay," my Dad says, still unsure about my plan.

"Kids want to have a voice in our town," I tell him.

"And you are that voice, Dane?"

"Yup. Someone's gotta do it."

"If you change the law, what will you do with your first legal snowball, Dane?"

I scratch my head. "Probably throw it at Dax," I say.

My dad shrugs his shoulders, "Really, Dane?"

"You can't argue with a genius at work, Dad. Now if you'll excuse me please, I have some intense work to do."

"Gosh, Dane what's next? Are you going to run for Mayor?"

"One thing at a time, Dad."

One.

  Thing.

    At.

     A.

      Time.

"INCOMING AGAIN, DAX!"

The next morning at breakfast I barely eat because I am too busy reviewing my notes.

"What's with all the papers?" Mom asks.

"My plan for how I'm going to overturn the snowball ban. I'm going to talk to my friends and get them involved too. I'm not the only one who wants snowball fights in Severance."

"Dane, I think this may be something for adults to handle," Mom tells me.

"It's been 100 years and no one has tried to change it so far," I say.

"Good point. How about this, talk with your friends and if you still want to change the law, we will support you 100%."

I hug my mom. "Thanks, Mom! I won't let you down."

"Dane, you could never let us down. Never."

As I put on my shoes for school, I can hear my parents talking at the table.

"I just don't want him to be upset if it doesn't work out," says Dad.

"What if it does? What if he's the one to make the change happen? If anyone can do it, it's Dane," Mom replies. "If a law was crazy enough to be put in place, maybe it takes someone crazy enough to reverse it?"

After hearing their conversation, I think to myself,

"I got this!"

I gather my friends at school. "Students of Range View Elementary, who would like to be able to throw a snowball without the fear of breaking the law?"

"Me!"

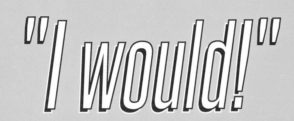

"I would!"

"Me too!"

I knew it! Everyone agrees with me.

"If you want to enjoy winter, like the rest of the country – wait, like the rest of the world – join me in a snowball revolution!"

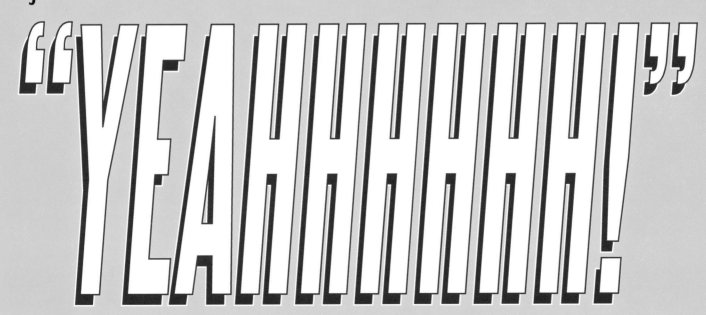

"YEAHHHHHHH!"

I tell everyone to write letters to the Mayor stating that the snowball ban needs to be overturned. If we get enough letters they'll have to listen to us.

Like I keep saying, kids want to know they have a voice in this town.

Now that I have my classmates on board, the bigger task is up to me. I must prepare a speech to present to the Severance Trustees all by myself.

Wait, public speaking? Like, in front of everyone?

Dear Mayor McLeod,

I feel the Severance snowball ban is an outdated law. The law was created many years ago. Today kids need reasons to play outside. In fact, research suggests that a lack of exposure to the outdoors can lead to obesity, ADHD, and anxiety. Kids want to have snowball fights without breaking the law. Kids want to have a voice in our town.

WHAT DID I GET MYSELF INTO?

I have to focus and remain calm. I can't allow my worrying to get the best of me. Like a pitcher in the bottom of the ninth trying to hold the lead, I will stare down the Trustees and throw the heat.

The next few days become crunch time. Every morning I wake up and recite my speech as I get ready for school. I even practice while I brush my teeth. There isn't a second that goes by that I am not focused on my mission.

Before I know it, the big day arrives. I wake up to find a chillier than usual day, with frost covering my window and the yard.

By the holidays, it will be snowing, just in time for everyone in Severance to have a legal snowball fight.

My mom knocks on the door with my freshly ironed shirt, and pants. "Are you ready, buddy?"

I stand proudly. "You know it, Mom!"

Checking myself in the mirror, I realize I am missing something. Grown ups wear suits and ties. If I am going to impress the Trustees, I have to look as professional as possible.

"**BOOM!** Now it's perfect," I say, smiling at my reflection.

When we arrive at Town Hall, I can't believe how many people are here. From local news, to family, to kids from my school, along with dozens of people from around town. It is like a Hollywood movie premier.

"Are you ready, Dane?" Mom asks.

"SO MANY people are here to watch me," I say looking at the crowd.

"They wouldn't have shown up if they didn't believe in you, Dane," Dad says.

"It's totally natural to be nervous," Mom adds. "Just like you do in sports, no matter how big the other team is, or how good the other players are, you always step up to the challenge. The same thing goes for your speech."

"Win or lose, you made it this far, and that's farther than anyone else ever has," Dad tells me.

"So, are you ready to make history, champ?" Mom asks with a smile.

I straighten my bow tie and smile back at them. "It's time to **change** history."

People shout at me from all directions as I step out of the car.

"Way to go Dane!"

"You can do this, Dane!"

"Throw a snowball at me, Dane!"

Inside I take a seat with my parents in the front row.

Mayor McLeod starts the meeting. "Today, we have Dane Best who would like to discuss Chapter 10, Article 5, Section 80. Dane, when you're ready, please step up to the podium."

I take a deep breath and look out at everyone gathered. I can feel their love all around me. Now, all I have to do is convince the trustees of the town to believe in me as well. I tell myself, *It's time to step up*.

And so I do.

Now is the time I've been waiting for. I begin my presentation, just as I've practiced.

"I am here today to hopefully change the law about throwing snowballs..."

"Today kids need reasons to play outside..."

"Kids want to have snowball fights without breaking the law..."

"Kids want to have a voice in our town."

I thank the Trustees for their time and sit back down, waiting for the official vote. If the majority of the Trustees agree with me, then I win and the ban will be lifted. I am frozen like a snowball, as Mayor McLeod asks each of the Trustees for their vote.

One by one, I hear, 'Yes'.

Each 'Yes' brings a wider grin to my face.

As the Mayor reaches the final person left to vote, I can hear my Mom gasp.

"I think we're going to win," she whispers.

"Don't jinx it!" Dad says.

Finally, the votes are all in and it is time for the Mayor to make it official.

Then it happens.

Mayor McLeod leans into the microphone, as the crowd waits eagerly. "It sounds like you have a unanimous pass. It sounds like you just changed the law, buddy."

The
Room
Erupts!

I did it! **We did it!** All the kids in Severance did it!

Now, there is only one thing left to do to make it really official. Outside, Mayor McLeod hands me a fresh snowball.

"Alright, Dane, throw your first snowball. The first legal one," he says.

I take the snowball and lean back. While cameras flash all around me, I launch the first legal snowball in 100 years, high into the Severance air. Even Dax throws one.

From now on, winter will have a new sense of freedom in Severance, and I can't wait to get together with all my friends for the biggest snowball fight the town has ever seen.

Today isn't only a victory for kids, but a win for anyone who has been told their voice isn't big enough, simply because of their age.

As we drive back home, nothing could erase the smile from my face. Sure, the snowball ban went my way, but this is just the beginning.

Now, about that whole "running for Mayor" thing my dad mentioned. Eh, maybe when I'm older.

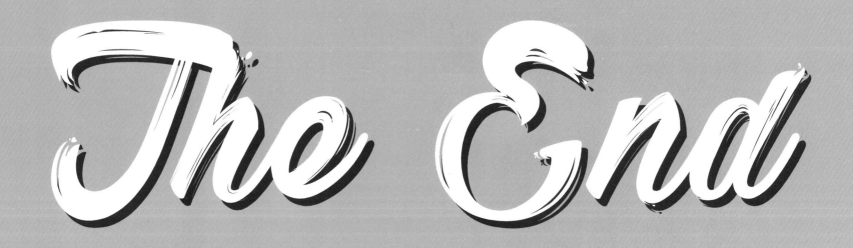

Get to know Dane Best

All about Dane's Family: My dad's name is Derrick, my mom's name is Brooke, and I have two brothers, Colby (older) and Dax (younger).

Dane's Favorite Part of Winter is: Sledding and throwing snowballs!

Dane's favorite sport: Basketball.

Dane's favorite foods: Antelope meat, artichoke, tomatoes, and chocolate chip mint ice cream.

Dane's favorite things about Severance: It's small, has lots of parks and a great fishing spot.

Dane's favorite type of music: Rap music.

Interesting fact about Dane: His favorite class in school is math. Dane loves trying to figure out math problems in his head.

If Dane was a superhero, his superpower would be: Reading people's minds.

If Dane could travel anywhere in the world, it would be: Australia.

ABOUT THE AUTHOR & ILLUSTRATOR: RICHIE FRIEMAN

Dubbed a "Modern Day Renaissance Man" by St. Martin's Press, Richie Frieman's career spans a life as an author, illustrator, artist, entrepreneur and even a professional wrestler. A #1 best selling and award winning author and illustrator of seven books, in multiple genres, his work has been sold on the shelves of Barnes & Noble, BAM!, Nordstrom and China (translated as well).

Born in Richmond, Virginia, Frieman was raised in Baltimore, Maryland, and attended The University of Maryland College Park, graduating in 2001 with a degree in Fine Arts. After graduation, Frieman dove head first into a career in the arts, immersing himself in all areas of illustration, painting, graphics, sculpture, and literature. Not content with sticking to one linear career path, Frieman launched an adventurous career, which included stints as a professional artist, author, illustrator, inventor, and even as an eight-year career as a professional wrestler, with the ring name, "The Thrill From Israel" Buster Maccabi where he earned more than a dozen titles in various federations throughout the country. After retiring from the ring in 2008, Frieman will get back into the squared circle in the fall of 2019, for one more match, all in the name of charity.

Despite his success in literature and the arts, Frieman grew up with a severe learning disability that made reading and comprehension an arduous task. In fact, Frieman never read a full book, cover to cover, until his senior year of college (ironically, it was a biography about a pro wrestler). However, despite his troubles, Frieman never lost his love for writing and pursuing a career as an author. He is very open about the difficulties he had in school and wants other children with similar issues to know they are not alone. He remains a constant advocate for literacy, education and the motto he lives by, "always dream bigger". His entertaining discussions to schools and organizations about his career has made him a sought after speaker.

Frieman has appeared globally on multiple high profile media outlets including MSNBC, Fox News, TIME, Forbes Magazine, The Wall Street Journal, Entrepreneur Magazine, USA Today, Fox Business News, Publishers Weekly, and Parade, just to name a few. Frieman currently lives in Baltimore, Maryland with his beautiful wife Jamie, their amazing daughter, Maddy, super-cool son, Cole, and an incredibly hyper puppy, Tucker. For more on Richie, his book and to contact him directly, please visit the sites below.

"Look the stars, then close your eyes. Breathe in deep and realize, if you wish enough and see it through, that wish you wished will come true." - **Richie Frieman**

RichieFrieman.com    **Facebook.com/RichieFrieman**   **@RichieFrieman**

Severence Town Law

Chapter 10, Article 5, Section 80

Before Dane Best persuaded his town officials to lift the outdated ban on throwing snowballs, the law stated:

"It is unlawful for any person to throw or shoot any stone or any other missile upon or at any person, animal, building, tree or other public or private property; or at or against any vehicle or equipment designed for the transportation of persons or property."

Discussion

These questions are designed to help parents and children actively engage in Dane's story. They are intended to spark conversation about laws (or rules), why they are important, and how citizens have the freedom to discuss with law makers why laws should be changed.

1. Have you ever been on a field trip with your school? Where did you go? Do you remember what you learned?
2. What is your favorite thing about the town you live in?
3. Have you ever thrown a snowball with family or friends? Describe who, what, when, where, and how.
4. Draw a picture of yourself throwing a snowball. Include family, friends, or pets who might be with you.
5. Write a story about throwing snowballs with family or friends. Include characters, a beginning, a middle, and an end.
6. How far can you throw a snowball?
7. The last time you threw snowballs, did you have fun? Talk about why or why not.
8. Recall how old the snowball ban was when Dane first heard of it on his field trip. How would you feel if throwing snowballs was illegal in your town?
9. Would you want to change the law if participating in this activity were illegal? Talk about how changing a law is possible.
10. Are you aware of laws in your town that may be outdated? How would you go about changing an outdated law in your town?

Color With Dane

What would you put inside of your snowglobe? What does winter look like at your house?

Color With Dane

Dane loves to wear his bowtie. How would you decorate your bowtie?

Color With Dane

What are you celebrating?

Color With Dane

My Winter Story

CPSIA information can be obtained at www.ICGtesting.com
Printed in the USA
LVIW011014010419
612518LV00002B/32